SCOTLAND'S GLORY
GLENCOE

SCOTLAND'S GLORY

The years from 1956 to 1969 could easily be described as Scotland's glory years. Scots men and women were winners in sport and leading lights in entertainment, while Scottish engineering led the way in construction and design.

These were also glory years for two of the nation's national treasures – The Broons and Oor Wullie. The couthy characters from the Fun Section of The Sunday Post were brought to life in laughter-packed stories, beautifully drawn by artist Dudley D. Watkins. So sit back, relax and journey through Scotland's glory years in the company of the family from Glebe Street and the wee laddie from Auchenshoogle.

THE BROONS and OOR WULLIE books continue to be published on alternate years and remain popular Christmas gifts. 2009 sees the publication of another fun-filled BROONS book. The characters also appear weekly in The Sunday Post.

Printed and published in Great Britain by DC Thomson & Co., Ltd.,
185 Fleet Street, London EC4A 2HS. © DC Thomson & Co., Ltd., 2009.
ISBN 978 1 84535 394 0

The Sunday Post 1st April 1956

The Sunday Post 29th April 1956

The Sunday Post 10th June 1956

The Sunday Post 8th July 1956

The Sunday Post 12th May 1957

OOR WULLIE   The Glory Years — 1957

The Sunday Post 20th January 1957

The Sunday Post 21st July 1957

The Sunday Post 24th February 1957

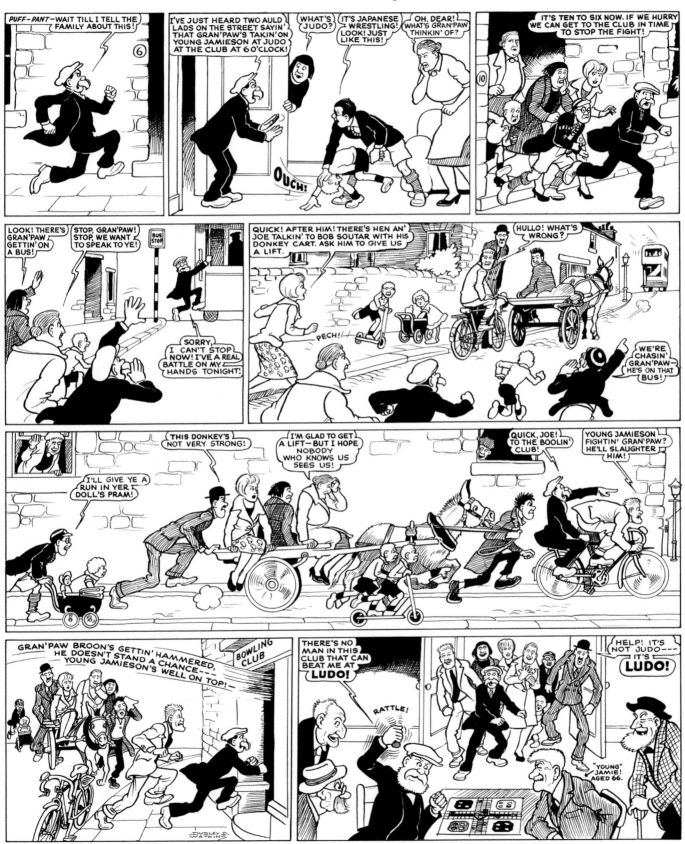

The Sunday Post 25th August 1957

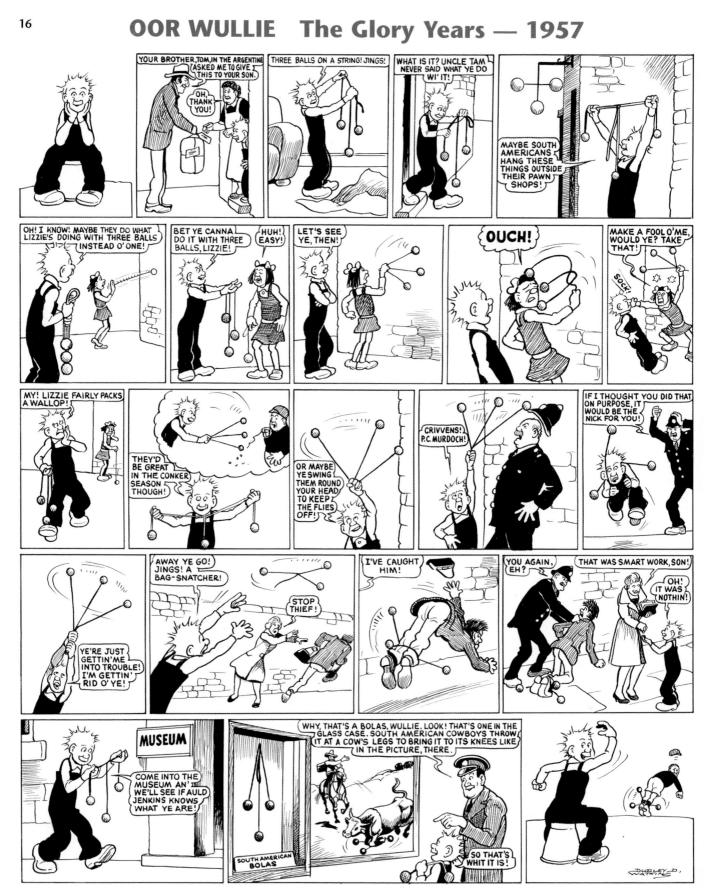

The Sunday Post 17th March 1957

The Sunday Post 17th November 1957

The Sunday Post 13th October 1957

OOR WULLIE   The Glory Years — 1958

The Sunday Post 6th July 1958

The Sunday Post 23rd February 1958

The Sunday Post 21st September 1958

The Sunday Post 16th March 1958

In 1965, Roy Williamson and Ronnie Browne formed The Corries, Scotland's most famous folk duo. 'Flower of Scotland', written by Williamson, has become the country's unofficial anthem.

One of the most popular television programmes in the 1960s was 'Doctor Finlay's Casebook', which starred Bill Simpson and Andrew Cruickshank.

Jackie Stewart, one of the greats of Formula One racing. He won his first grand prix in 1965, and the first of three World Championships in 1969.

Edinburgh Castle. Perched on an extinct volcano, this instantly-recognisable building is one of Scotland's most popular tourist attractions.

Glory in Lisbon, May 25th, 1967. Celtic's Steve Chalmers scores the winning goal in the European Cup Final against Inter Milan. Celtic won four trophies that season and became the first British club to win the European Cup.

In the early 1960s, Edinburgh-born Sean Connery found fame as James Bond Agent 007, licensed to kill. The first of his seven Bond movies was 'Dr No' which was released in 1962.

OOR WULLIE   The Glory Years — 1958

The Sunday Post 12th October 1958

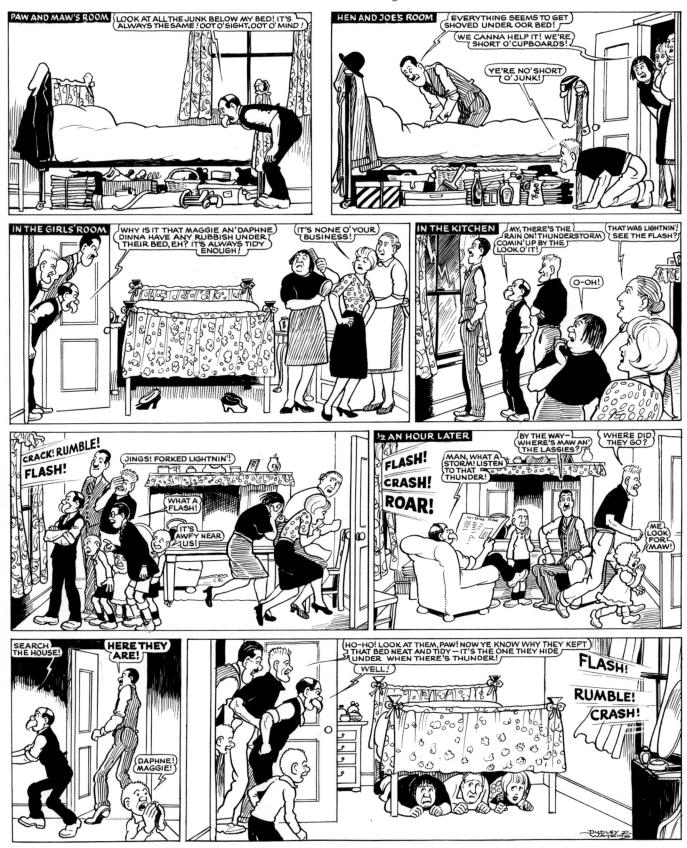

The Sunday Post 28th September 1958

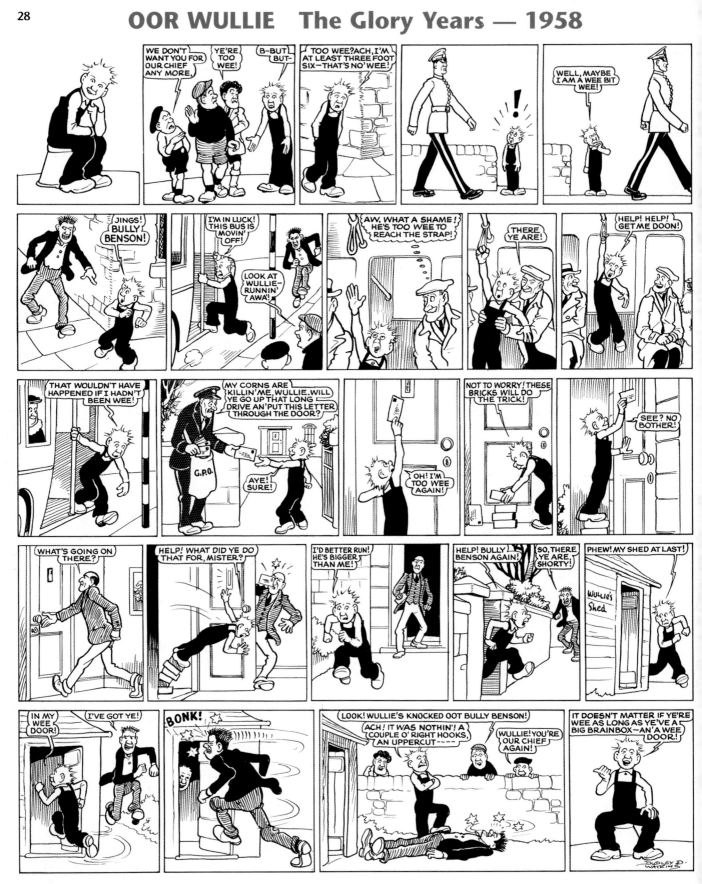

The Sunday Post 16th November 1958

The Sunday Post 15th February 1959

The Sunday Post 25th January 1959

The Sunday Post 22nd February 1959

The Sunday Post 12th April 1959

The Sunday Post 16th August 1959

The Sunday Post 24th May 1959

The Sunday Post 29th November 1959

The Sunday Post 16th August 1959

The Sunday Post 24th July 1960

The Sunday Post 14th February 1960

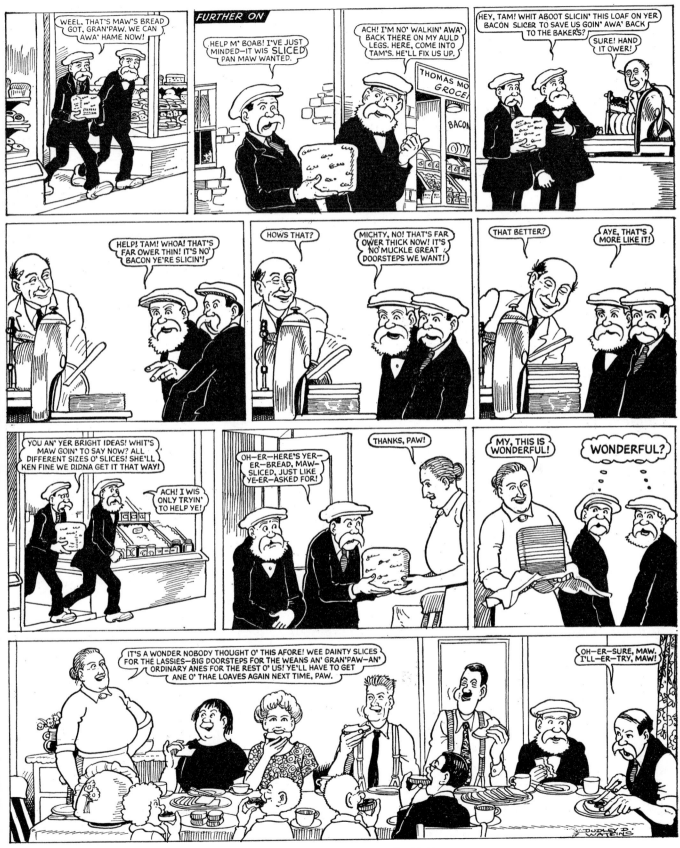

The Sunday Post 31st July 1960

The Sunday Post 22nd May 1960

The Sunday Post 18th September 1960

The Sunday Post 28th August 1960

THE BROONS   The Glory Years — 1960

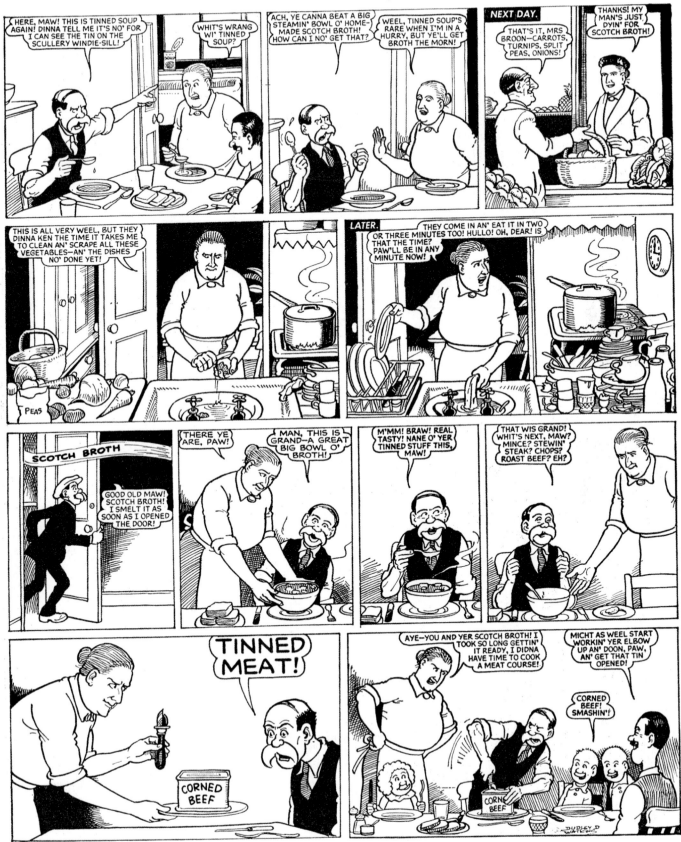

The Sunday Post 4th December 1960

The Sunday Post 22nd January 1961

The Sunday Post 5th March 1961

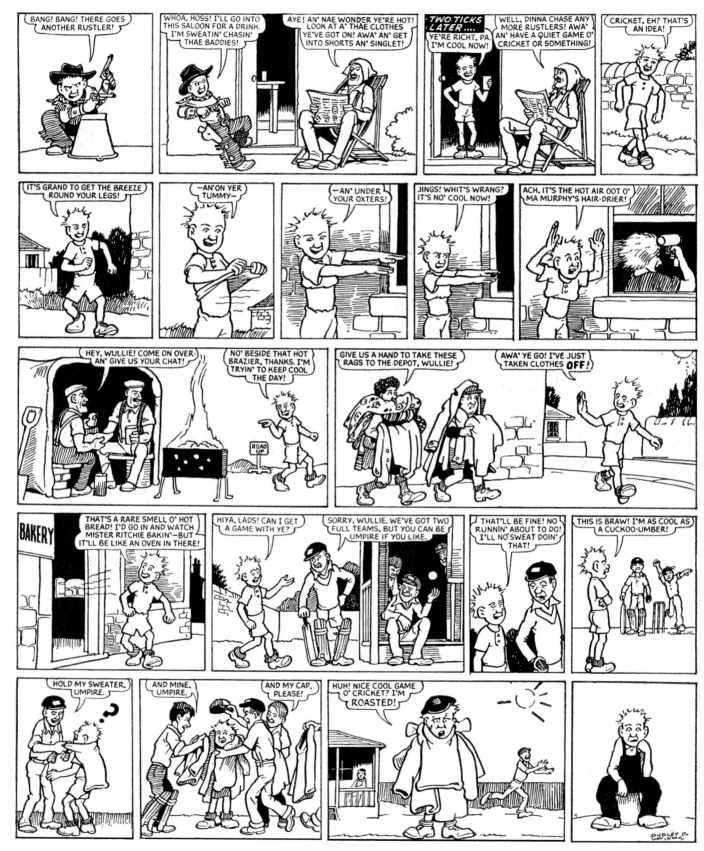

The Sunday Post 4th June 1961

The Sunday Post 7th May 1961

OOR WULLIE   The Glory Years — 1961

The Sunday Post 8th October 1961

The Sunday Post 20th August 1961

OOR WULLIE   The Glory Years — 1961

The Sunday Post 26th November 1961

The Sunday Post 29th April 1962

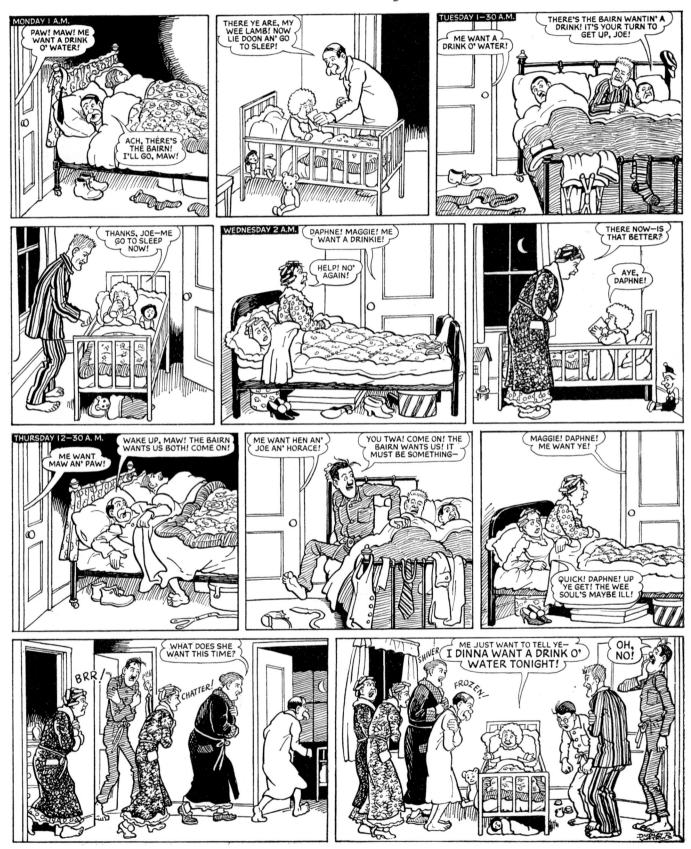

The Sunday Post 8th April 1962

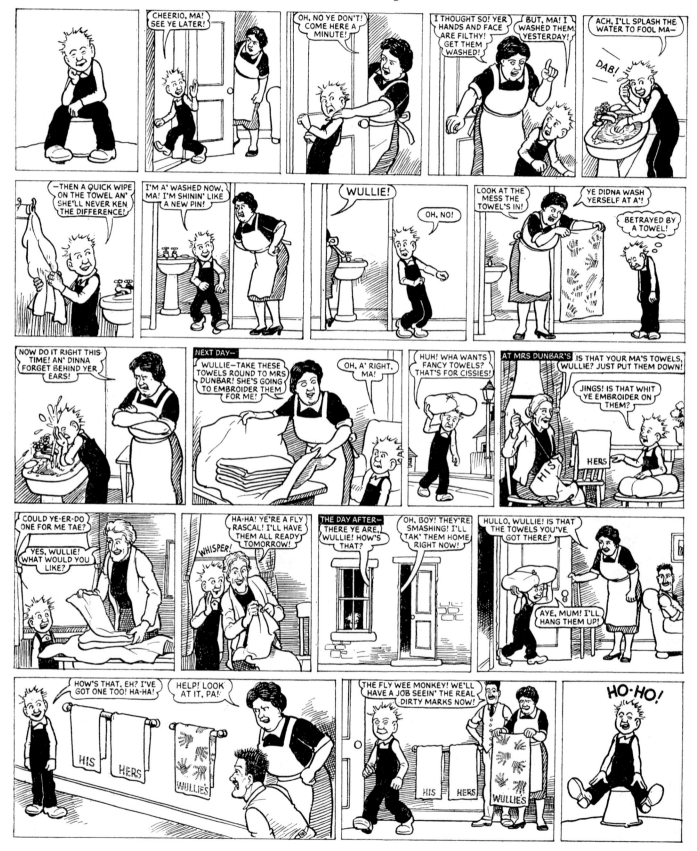

The Sunday Post 26th August 1962

The Sunday Post 7th October 1962

The Sunday Post 11th November 1962

al's a bolt ...

urglar running ...

"Hey, waiter! This steak's so tough I can't get my fork into it."

"Well, that's not so bad, sir. At the place across the road you can't get your fork into the gravy!"

★ ★ ★

Sam—"I told teacher today that I was an only child."

Pa—"And what did he say to that?"

Sam—"Thank goodness!"

★ ★ ★

Absent-Minded Man (at fire station)—"Could you direct me to the nearest telephone? My house is on fire and I want to phone for ..."

...an, can you tell ... Inverness? ... oing there. Just ...

"What do you ... w play? It had a ... ding, didn't it?" ...—"Yes. Every- ... appy when it ...

Police Sergeant—"How do ... for having all this ... your pockets?"

...uspect—"Well, y'see, ... sideboard at ...

...man broke ... find out who ... him ...

Teacher—"Now that I ... finished my lesson on the ... is there anything anyo... would like to ask me?"

Joan—"Please, miss, w... don't the little fish dro... before they learn to swim?"

★ ★ ★

Unpopular army sergeant ... rifle practice)—"That bull... just missed me!"

Recruit—"I'm awfully sor... sergeant!"

★ ★ ★

Boss—"Now, my boy, ar... you the boss of this business?"

Boy—"No, sir."

Boss—"Then don't talk lik... an idiot!"

★ ★ ★

Policeman—"Move along... No begging allowed here!"

...—"What! It isn't my... I hold my hand out ... s raining and a lady ... enny in it!"

1963

...d McLeod get his play ...

...es, the stage manager ... up the manuscript and ... t in a snowstorm scene!"

John—"Hey! What's the idea of wearing my new rain-coat?"

Bob—"Well, you wouldn't like your new suit to get wet, would you?"

Sportsman—"S... Milligan, why didn't ... me this horse was ... I bought it?" ... Milligan ...

"Mother says will you give me the brush you borrowed from us last Thursday?"

"Yes, but don't forget to bring it back!"

★ ★ ★

Mother—"Don't fire that arrow at Billy's stomach!"

Eck—"But we're playing at William Tell, and he's eaten the apple!"

...you want a job on my ...

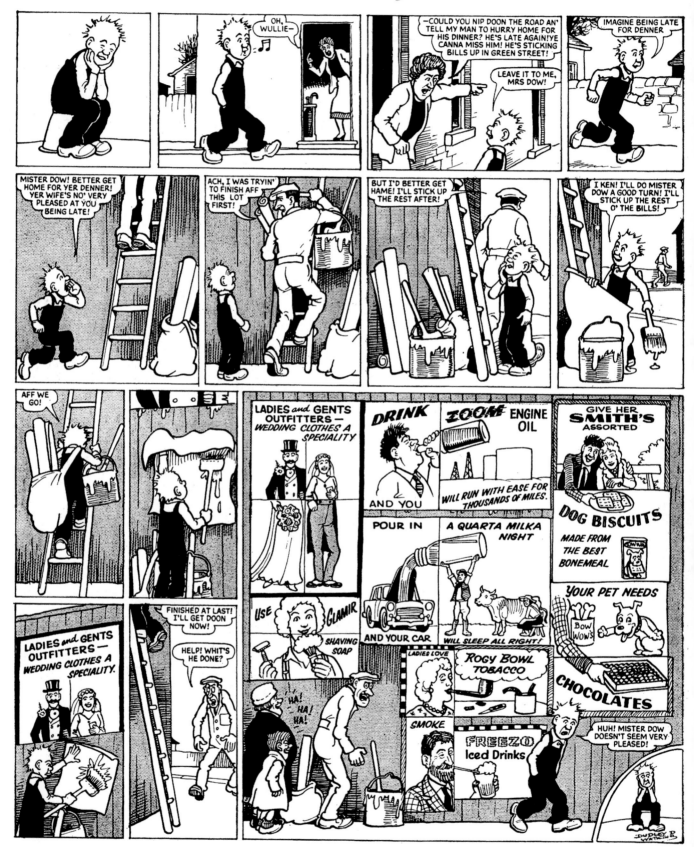

The Sunday Post 13th January 1963

The Sunday Post 3rd February 1963

The Sunday Post 17th February 1963

The Sunday Post 14th July 1963

SCOTLAND'S GLORY

PEOPLE AND PLACES THAT MAKE SCOTLAND GREAT

The day Scotland became unofficial football world champions! England had won the World Cup in 1966 but, on April 11th, 1967, goals from Denis Law, Bobby Lennox and Jim McCalliog ensured England's first loss since lifting the Jules Rimet trophy.

The Glasgow Pavilion was one the jewels of Scottish theatre during the 1960s. A host of music hall legends appeared here and for years the theatre has been one of the homes of the traditional Christmas pantomime.

Marie McDonald McLaughlin Lawrie, better known as Lulu. In the sixties, this Scots singer took the pop world by storm. As well as having a string of top ten hits, she was also joint winner of the Eurovision Song Contest in 1969.

Enjoy the winter beauty of Dirrie More, a mountain pass near Braemore in Highland Region, one of many examples of Scotland's natural beauty.

Scots actor David McCallum shot to fame as Illya Kuryakin in The Man From U.N.C.L.E. which was a favourite television programme from 1964-1968. He also appeared in many films, notably with Steve McQueen in The Great Escape which was released in 1963.

The Sunday Post 26th May 1963

The Sunday Post 1st December 1963

The Sunday Post 1st September 1963

OOR WULLIE   The Glory Years — 1964

The Sunday Post 19th January 1964

The Sunday Post 1st March 1964

OOR WULLIE   The Glory Years — 1964

The Sunday Post 1st March 1964

The Sunday Post 12th April 1964

The Sunday Post 24th May 1964

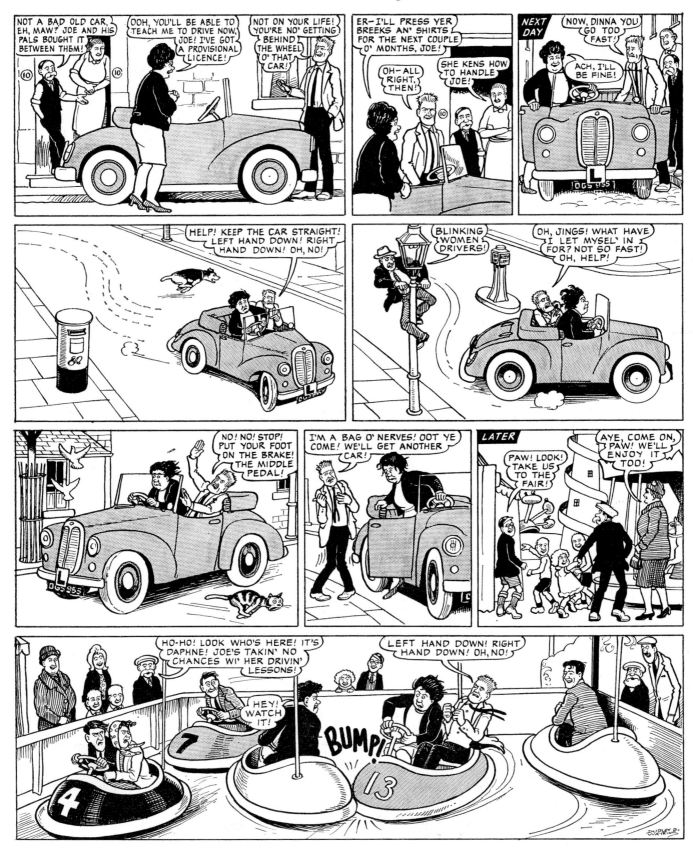

The Sunday Post 26th April 1964

The Sunday Post 18th October 1964

The Sunday Post 2nd August 1964

The Sunday Post 28th February 1965

The Sunday Post 17th January 1965

The Sunday Post 9th May 1965

The Sunday Post 18th July 1965

The Sunday Post 17th October 1965

The Sunday Post 29th August 1965

The Sunday Post 19th December 1965

The Sunday Post 21st November 1965

OOR WULLIE   The Glory Years — 1966

The Sunday Post 9th January 1966

The Sunday Post 6th February 1966

The Sunday Post 15th May 1966

The Sunday Post 13th March 1966

OOR WULLIE   The Glory Years — 1966

The Sunday Post 3rd July 1966

The Sunday Post 29th May 1966

The Sunday Post 11th December 1966

The Sunday Post 26th March 1967

The Sunday Post 8th January 1967

The Sunday Post 21st May 1967

The Sunday Post 2nd April 1967

The Sunday Post 26th November 1967

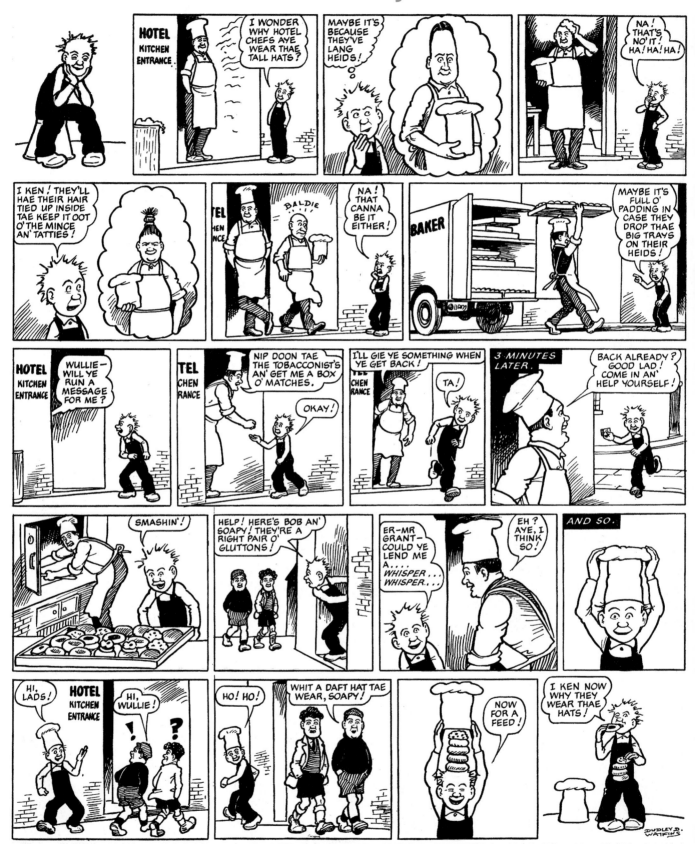

The Sunday Post 7th May 1967

The Sunday Post 17th December 1967

The Sunday Post 10th December 1967

The Sunday Post 18th February 1968

The Sunday Post 11th February 1968

OOR WULLIE The Glory Years — 1968

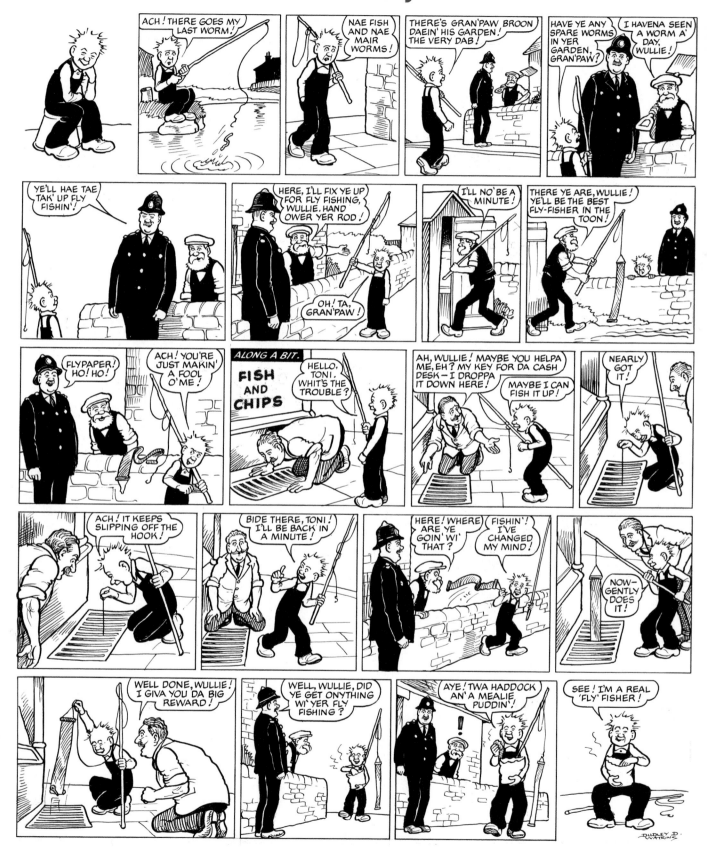

The Sunday Post 7th April 1968

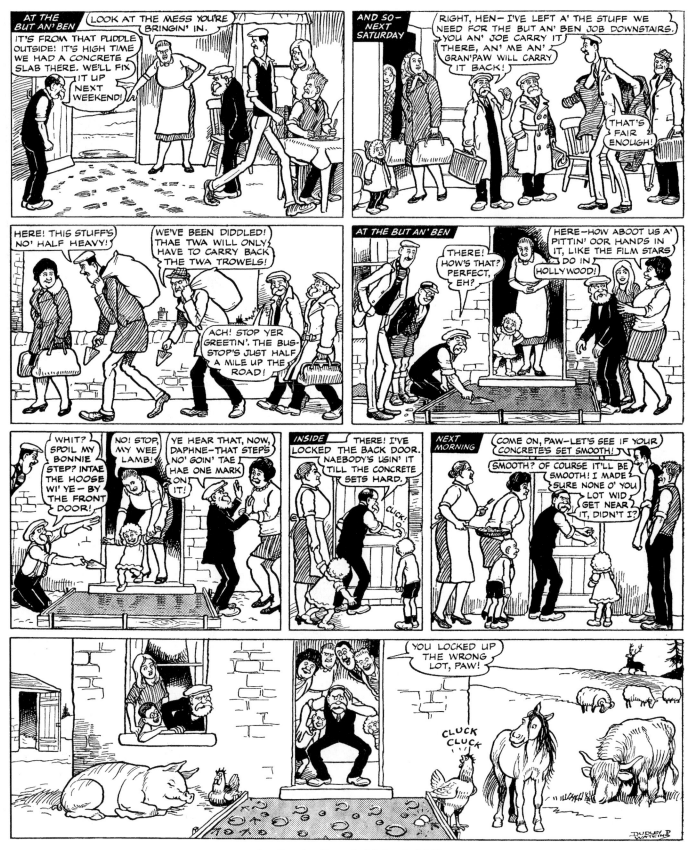

The Sunday Post 3rd March 1968

SCOTLAND'S GLORY

PEOPLE AND PLACES THAT MAKE SCOTLAND GREAT

Andy Stewart shot to fame as the presenter of television's The White Heather Club which ran from 1958 to 1968, turning the young Scotsman into an international star.

Tarbert, Kintyre, one of the many picturesque fishing villages dotted around the coast of Scotland.

Francie and Josie, alias the inimitable Rikki Fulton and Jack Milroy. These comedians were great favourites throughout the Glasgow theatre scene during the 1960s.

In 1968, Marmalade became the first Scottish pop group to reach number one in the UK charts with a cover version of The Beatles' Ob-La-Di, Ob-La-Da.

Glasgow-born actress Deborah Kerr found fame as Anna Leonowens, playing opposite Yul Brynner in the film version of 'The King and I', which was released in 1956.

Dundonian Dick McTaggart won boxing's Lightweight gold medal in the 1956 Melbourne Olympics, Commonwealth gold in 1958 and the European Championship in 1961.

OOR WULLIE The Glory Years — 1968

The Sunday Post 19th May 1968

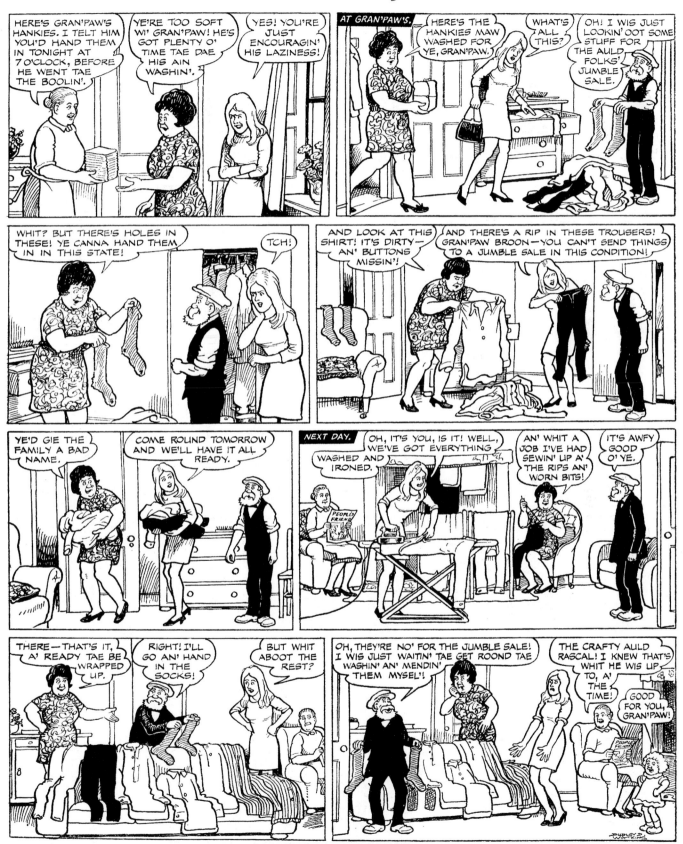

The Sunday Post 25th August 1968

OOR WULLIE   The Glory Years — 1968

The Sunday Post 25th August 1968

The Sunday Post 6th October 1968

The Sunday Post 30th March 1969

OOR WULLIE The Glory Years — 1969

The Sunday Post 16th February 1969

The Sunday Post 20th April 1969

The Sunday Post 3rd August 1969

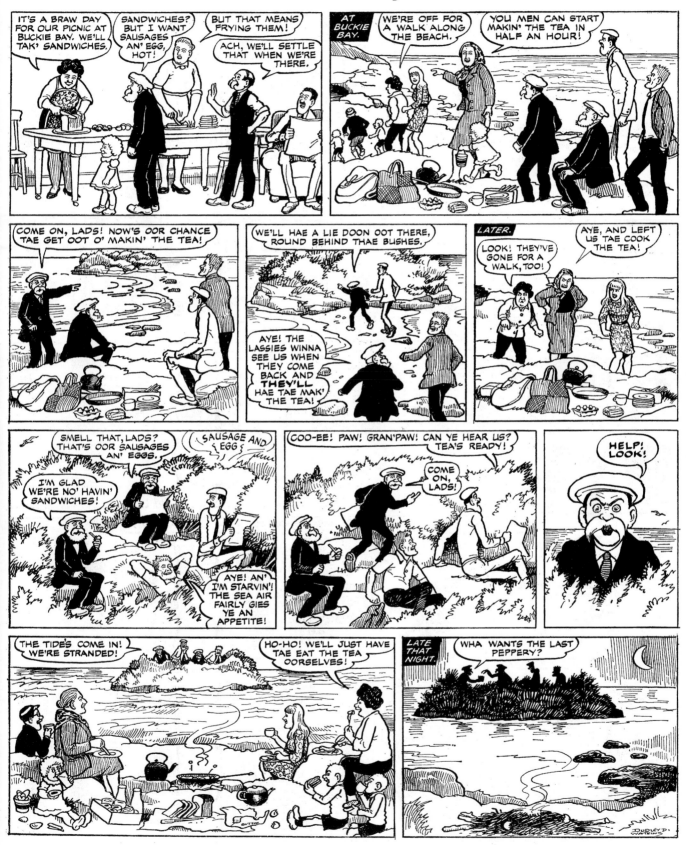

The Sunday Post 25th May 1969

SCOTLAND'S GLORY
FORTH ROAD BRIDGE